Dad got a boat.

Everyone sat in the boat.

Dad pushed the boat out.

Oh no! Dad was stuck.

Mum pulled Dad. Wilma pushed
the boat.

They went down the river. Nobody got wet.

"What a good job!" said Mum.

They had a picnic.

It began to rain. But nobody
got wet.

The boat floated away.

"Oh no!" gasped Mum. "Help me get the boat."

Mum pulled the boat in.

"Don't let me fall in," said Mum.

Mum didn't get wet.

"Nobody got wet," said Dad.
It was time to go home.

Oh no! Everyone got wet!